Violin Exam Pieces

ABRSM Grade 4

Selected from the 2012–2015 syllabus

Name

Date of exam

C000089930

Contents

Violin consultant: Philippa Bunting
Footnotes: Edward Huws Jones (EHJ), Richard Jones (RJ) and Anthony Burton

---

Other pieces for Grade 4

LIST A

4 **Corelli** Allemanda: 2nd movt from Sonata in F, Op. 5 No. 10. Corelli, *12 Sonatas*, Op. 5, Vol. 2 (Schott)

5 **J. Gibbs** Aria *and* Variation 3: from Sonata in D minor, Op. 1 No. 1. *Sheila M. Nelson's Baroque Violinist* (Boosey & Hawkes)

6 **F. M. Veracini** Largo e nobile: 1st movt from Sonata No. 1 in F (1716). Veracini, *12 Sonatas for Recorder/Flute/Violin*, Vol. 1 (Peters)

LIST B

4 **C. Dancla** Rondo (from Introduction and Rondo): No. 12 from *Petite école de la mélodie*, Op. 123, Vol. 2 (Schott) or *First Repertoire for Violin*, arr. Cohen (Faber)

5 **Kreisler** Sicilienne: from Sicilienne and Rigaudon (in the style of Francoeur). Published separately or *Fritz Kreisler Repertoire*, Vol. 1 (Schott)

6 **A. Thomas** Gavotte (from *Mignon*). No. 9 from *Suzuki Violin School*, Vol. 2 (Alfred – Summy-Birchard)

LIST C

4 **Kabalevsky** Scherzo, arr. Sorokin. No. 18 from *Kabalevsky Album Pieces* (Peters)

5 **Trad. Bosnian** The Sultan's Throne (violin melody). *Sevdah*, arr. Huws Jones and Velagić (Boosey & Hawkes)

6 **Pam Wedgwood** Falling: from *After Hours – Violin* (Faber)

First published in 2011 by ABRSM (Publishing) Ltd, a wholly owned subsidiary of ABRSM, 24 Portland Place, London W1B 1LU, United Kingdom

© 2011 by The Associated Board of the Royal Schools of Music

Music origination by Andrew Jones
Cover by Økvik Design
Printed in England by Halstan & Co. Ltd, Amersham, Bucks.

Estampie royal

Arranged by Edward Huws Jones

Anon. 13th-century French

Most of the surviving medieval dance music is written in the form of an estampie. A short phrase (bars 1–2) is answered by an 'open' refrain (bars 3–5) and then repeated (bars 6–7) with a 'closed' refrain (bars 8–11). A new phrase is then introduced – or improvised – with the original open and closed refrains and the process continues as long as the players and dancers wish. Dances such as these would probably be accompanied by drone instruments (bagpipes or hurdy gurdies) and percussion instruments, both of which are suggested in this simple piano accompaniment. EHJ

Musette

Third movement from Sonata in G, Op. 1 No. 8

A:2

Arranged by Ferdinand David

Jean-Marie Leclair

The French violinist, composer and dancer Jean-Marie Leclair (1697–1764) was born in Lyons, travelled widely during his career, and died in Paris, murdered outside his house. The crime remained unsolved at the time, although the evidence is said to point to a nephew with whom Leclair had quarrelled. Musically, Leclair was well known for importing the Italian style of composing and violin-playing into French music, which had its own strong traditions. The first publication in which he did this was a set of 12 sonatas for violin and keyboard, printed in Paris in 1723. The Musette from the eighth sonata is named after a small bagpipe popular in French chamber music at the time, and includes melodic ornamentation and drone basses suggesting the instrument. This arrangement, including the invention of the piano part above the bass line, is by one of the great German violinist-composers of the 19th century, Ferdinand David (1810–73) – for whom Mendelssohn wrote his famous Violin Concerto.

© 1981 by The Associated Board of the Royal Schools of Music
Reproduced from *First Violin*, Book III (ABRSM)

AB 3583

Adagio

First movement from Sonata No. 5 in C minor

Edited by and continuo realized by
Peter Holman

William McGibbon

The Scottish violinist and composer William McGibbon (1696–1756) was a leading figure in the musical life of Edinburgh for many years. His works include sets of variations on Scottish tunes as well as sonatas in the Italian style – a style that he may have absorbed on a visit to Italy, as well as through his studies with sonata composer William Corbett. This is the opening movement of the fifth in a set of 'Six Sonatas or Solos for a German flute or Violin and a Bass', published in Edinburgh in 1740. The editor, Peter Holman, has included one possible version of the right-hand keyboard part, based on the figures under the bass line. With the exception of the last slur in bar 2 and the slur in bar 4, the phrasing is as in the original, and may be supplemented according to taste. The dynamics are suggestions for exam purposes and may be varied.

Mélodie

from *Méthode de violon*, Op. 102

B:1

Arranged by Nico Dezaire and Gunter van Rompaey

Charles-Auguste de Bériot

Charles-Auguste de Bériot (1802–70) was a well-known Belgian violinist and composer, who in his playing and his music enhanced the elegant French style of the time with Romantic expressiveness and some of the technical innovations of Paganini. He wrote not only ten concertos and other showpieces for violin, but also a number of instruction books. The first part of his 1858 *Méthode de violon*, Op. 102, later published separately as a 'Violin Method for Beginners', is the source of this 'Melody'. It originally had an accompaniment for a second violin, which in this version has been expanded into a piano part by Nico Dezaire.

Scherzo

Third movement from Sonatina in G, Op. 100

Edited by Richard Jones

Antonín Dvořák

The great Czech composer Antonín Dvořák (1841–1904) spent the years 1892–5 in America as director and composition teacher at the National Conservatory of Music, New York. During this American period he composed, among other things, the 'New World' Symphony, the Cello Concerto, and the Violin Sonatina, Op. 100 (from which this Scherzo is selected), which dates from 1893 and was originally intended for his own children to play. In the violin part of bars 17–31, the slur to the last pair of quavers is editorial. RJ

Source: *Sonatine für Violine und Pianoforte*, Op. 100 (Berlin: N. Simrock, 1894)

Ambleside

from *A Tuneful Introduction to the Third Position*

Neil Mackay

Piano accompaniment by
Richard Allain

B:3

This melody is one of 24 in the 1963 publication *A Tuneful Introduction to the Third Position* by the Scottish-born violinist and teacher Neil Mackay (1922–73). The piano part is from a set written much later to accompany those tunes by Richard Allain (born 1965), Director of Music at Norwich School and a composer best known for his choral music. Ambleside is a town just north of Lake Windermere in the beautiful Lake District of north-west England.

An Alpine Tune

David Matthews

David Matthews (born 1943) is one of the major British composers of his generation; his large output includes seven symphonies and many other works for orchestra, two violin concertos and concertos for oboe and cello, and 12 string quartets. Early in his career, with his composer brother Colin, he assisted Deryck Cooke in making the first performing version of the unfinished Tenth Symphony by Gustav Mahler. And Mahler also figures in the background of this piece, which Matthews composed in October 2007 for a volume in the ABRSM *Spectrum* series. He says about it: 'I wrote the melody for *An Alpine Tune* in the Italian Dolomites, near to where Mahler wrote *Das Lied von der Erde* and his last two symphonies. It is an inspiring landscape. I also used the tune in my Sixth Symphony.'

© 2009 by Faber Music Ltd, London WC1B 3DA
Reproduced by permission of the publishers. All rights reserved. All enquiries about this piece, apart from those directly relating to the exams, should be addressed to Faber Music, Bloomsbury House, 74–77 Great Russell Street, London WC1B 3DA.
Reproduced from *Spectrum for Violin* (ABRSM)

King Boogie

No. 6 from *The Christopher Norton Concert Collection for Violin*

Christopher Norton

Christopher Norton was born in New Zealand in 1953, and came to Britain in 1977 to study at York University. He has become well known for his educational music for piano and various other instruments, including the *Microjazz*, *Microstyles*, *Big Beats* and *Concert Collection* series. The title of this piece from his violin *Concert Collection*, published in 2008, refers to boogie-woogie, a style of piano blues popular for dancing in the 1930s and '40s. The melody hints at the famous Christmas carol 'Good King Wenceslas'. The phrase 'shuffle style' in the tempo marking indicates swung rhythms rather than equal quavers.

Congratulations to the Bridegroom and Bride

C:3

Arranged by Ilana Cravitz

Trad. klezmer

D.S. al Fine

The klezmer style of instrumental music originated in the Jewish communities of central and eastern Europe in the 19th century, and subsequently became popular in the United States, picking up rhythmic syncopations and other elements of jazz. Klezmer music is particularly associated with weddings, and *Congratulations to the Bridegroom and Bride* ('Khosn kale mazltov' in Yiddish) is traditionally played at the end of a ceremony, when the guests shout out their congratulations. The melody is modal, that is with a scale other than the major and minor of European classical music. This version comes from a collection called *Klezmer Fiddle – a how-to guide* by Ilana Cravitz.

Variation is a characteristic element of klezmer playing; a passage is rarely performed exactly the same way twice. For this reason, candidates may prefer to observe the ornaments in bars 3–9 on the *dal segno* only. The dynamics shown here are suggestions and may be varied. The trills should be short, starting on the main note and played on the beat.